ILLUSTRATED CLASSICS

THE ADVENTURES OF KING ARTHUR AND HIS KNIGHTS

THOMAS MALORY

ADAPTED BY ANNE ROONEY · ILLUSTRATED BY CATHARINE COLLINGRIDGE

Sandy Creek
NEW YORK

Introduction

These stories tell the adventures of King Arthur and his knights. They tell of challenging events that seem to happen by chance and that test a knight's valor and virtue. If he is brave, good, strong, and makes the right choices, the adventure is a success. If he is cowardly, if he cheats, or if he is rude, the adventure goes badly.

Born to Be King

Long ago, in the time of castles and knights, of battles and magic and love, Uther Pendragon was king of England. He was in love with the beautiful Igrain. But she was married to the Duke of Cornwall. To marry her, he would have to get rid of her husband first.

So Uther Pendragon gathered a great army and marched to the Duke of Cornwall's castle. The Duke sent his wife to a different castle, at Tintagel, for her safety. Then he defended his castle against Uther's assault. Many died on both sides in the battle. Uther grew so sick with love that his knights sent for the wizard Merlin.

"I know you are in love with Igrain," Merlin said to the king. "I will make it happen that you marry her. But in return, you must give me the first child that you have together to raise as I choose."

Uther was so desperate that he agreed to Merlin's terrible request. That night, the Duke of Cornwall was killed in the battle.

Now that she was a widow, Igrain married Uther. She grieved silently for her first husband while she married her second. Nine months later, she gave birth to a boy. Merlin reminded the king of his promise. With a heavy heart, Uther agreed to hand over baby Arthur.

Merlin sent the knight Sir Ector to see Uther. He promised to bring Arthur up as if he were his own son. The king gave Sir Ector a bag of treasures, and the baby was wrapped in a cloth of gold and sent away.

Two years later, the king fell ill. All his enemies took advantage of his illness to wage war against him. Uther's army fought valiantly, but the king was very sick. Merlin came to him.

"Shall your son, Arthur, be king after you?" he asked.

The king said that he should be, and with those words he died.

There was great unrest in the country for many years as all the nobles fought to become king. At last, Merlin told the Archbishop of Canterbury that he must call all the lords and nobles to London for Christmas, and that they would see a marvelous miracle.

When the lords and nobles all gathered in a London churchyard, they were astonished to see a great marble stone, topped with an anvil. Sticking from the anvil was a great sword. Around it were letters traced in gold:

"Whosoever pulls this sword from the stone and anvil is the right-born king of all England."

The Sword in the Stone

The Archbishop of Canterbury declared a tournament, after which the knights would try to draw the sword from the stone.

Sir Ector brought his son, Sir Kay, and Arthur to the tournament. Kay had left his sword at home and sent Arthur to fetch it, but everyone was out.

"I can't leave my brother without a sword," Arthur said. "I will take the sword I saw in the churchyard."

Arthur easily slid the sword from the stone and anvil, and carried it to Sir Kay. Sir Kay recognized it and went straight to Sir Ector, saying:

"Look! Here is the sword from the stone—I must be the king!"

Sir Ector made Sir Kay swear how he got the sword.

"My brother Arthur gave it to me," he admitted.

"How did you get it?" Sir Ector asked Arthur.

"I saw it sticking out of a stone, and my brother needed a sword, so I took it," Arthur answered.

"Then you are the true-born king of all this land," Sir Ector said, "for no man can draw this sword except he who should be king."

Ector explained how Merlin had told him to bring Arthur up. Arthur wept upon learning that Ector was not his real father. They put the sword back in the stone.

When the knights tried to draw the sword, none succeeded. Only Arthur could take it.

Excalibur

Some of the nobles were happy to accept Arthur as king, but many grumbled and asked Merlin why a beardless boy should be their king. They complained it was done by witchcraft and was not fair. So they joined together and waged war on Arthur and his allies for many years. The battle was fierce, and thousands died before Merlin used his magic to stop it.

"Enough have died," he told Arthur. "It is time to stop. They will not trouble you for a few years."

King Arthur lived peacefully in his castle in Camelot, while his knights went on adventures. One day, a badly wounded knight came into the court. He had been hurt by a knight who stayed near a fountain, waiting for knights to fight. Another young knight rode out to the fountain, but he too returned injured. Angered, the king himself rode out to challenge the knight.

Arthur arrived at the fountain and struck on a shield hanging from a tree to summon the knight. The two fought, first with lances on horseback and then, when Arthur's lance broke, they fought with swords on foot. At last, Arthur's sword broke in two. The other knight pulled off Arthur's helmet and would have killed him, but Merlin appeared.

"Don't kill him," Merlin said, "for he is King Arthur." But still the knight raised his sword.

Merlin froze the knight by magic so that he fell into a coma. Then he took Arthur to a hermit to have his wounds healed.

When Arthur was better, he said to Merlin:

"Now I have no sword."

"There is a sword nearby for you," Merlin answered.

As they rode, they came to a lake. To Arthur's astonishment, an arm rose from the water, holding a beautiful sword in a jeweled scabbard.

"This is the sword I spoke of," Merlin said. A lady walked toward them over the lake.

"The Lady of the Lake will give you the sword if you do as she says," Merlin told Arthur.

"Lady," Arthur said. "I would like that sword."

"You may have it if you promise to give me a gift when I ask for it," the lady said. Arthur agreed.

So he took a boat that was moored nearby and rowed across the lake. When he took the sword, the hand disappeared below the water.

Merlin told him that the sword was called Excalibur, and it would be Arthur's sword for his whole life. As they rode on, Merlin asked whether Arthur liked the sword or the scabbard best. Arthur chose the sword.

"There you are wrong," Merlin said, "for you should prefer the scabbard. While you are wearing it, you will never die or shed any blood in battle." And the two men rode back to Arthur's castle.

The Adventures of Balin

One day, a young lady came to Arthur's court carrying a heavy sword.

"This sword is a nuisance to me," she said. "But only a true, pure, and brave knight can draw it."

King Arthur, and then all his knights, tried to draw the sword. None succeeded until the poorest knight, Balin, pulled it easily from the scabbard. The lady asked for it back, but Balin refused.

"You are unwise to keep it," she said, "for with it, you will kill the person you love best in the world."

Just then, the Lady of the Lake rode into court and reminded Arthur of his promise of a gift. She said:

"I demand the head of Balin or of that lady."

Arthur was horrified, and even more so when Balin, using his new sword, sliced off the Lady of the Lake's head. Arthur made Balin leave the court immediately.

After some time, Balin came to a castle where he was allowed to stay for the night if he would fight a powerful knight. The next morning, he put on his armor and borrowed a large shield. Balin and the mysterious knight fought long and hard, but were equally matched. They were both dying when Balin asked his opponent's name.

"I am Balan," he said, "brother to Balin."

"Oh, Balan, my brother—it is true! With this sword I have killed the person I love best in the world. If I had kept my own shield you would have recognized me."

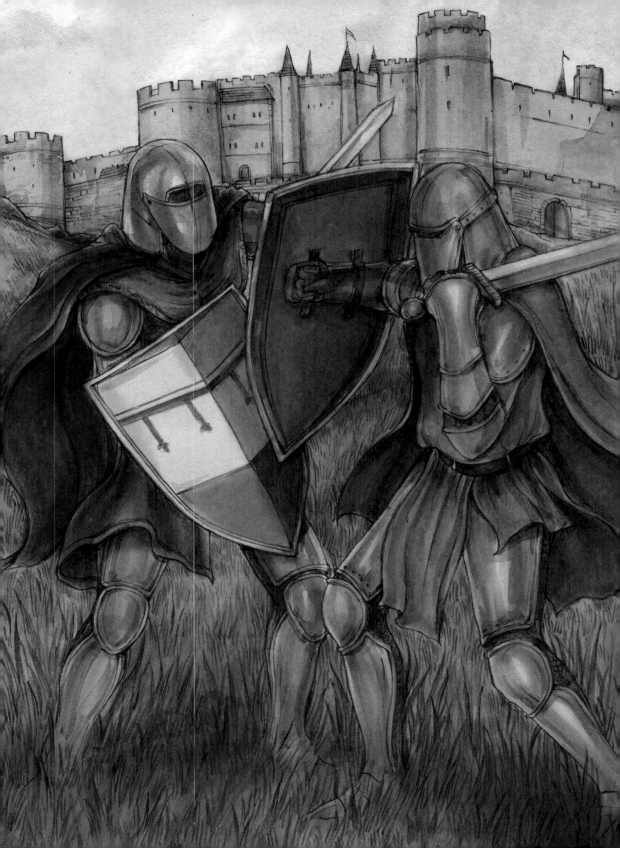

The Round Table

King Arthur was a young man, and it was natural that he should marry. Arthur had fallen in love with Guinevere, the beautiful daughter of King Lodegrean. Merlin warned him against the marriage, saying that it would all end badly. But Arthur was certain—he was so much in love—and so the marriage was arranged.

Guinevere arrived with a host of ladies and knights, all dressed in gorgeous, ornate clothes of silk and jewels. She brought with her a huge round table made of wood, a wedding gift from her father. It was large enough to seat 150 knights. King Lodegrean sent 100 of his own best knights to sit at the table, and Arthur vowed to gather together the greatest company of knights the world had ever seen. They must all be brave, honorable, and excellent in battle.

But the table was magical. At each place, the name of the knight who should sit there appeared mysteriously, in gold letters. Merlin explained:

"Some of these places will not be filled for many years. And this place"—he pointed to a seat—"is called the 'Siege Perilous.' It will be occupied by the purest knight. Anyone else who sits there will die. The seat *beside* it is for the greatest knight in the world, but he will not be the most pure."

Sir Lancelot

The wedding feast lasted many days. The knights jousted and danced, went hunting and hawking, and enjoyed many other festivities. In honor of his wedding, Arthur made his nephew, Gawain, a knight, and he took his seat at the Round Table where his name appeared.

Over time, more knights came to the court. One of those was Lancelot. As a baby, Lancelot had been stolen by the Lady of the Lake, who raised him. When he was old enough, she sent him to King Arthur's court, where Sir Gawain urged his uncle to accept Lancelot as a knight.

As Lancelot approached the Round Table, his name appeared in gold letters on the seat *beside* the Siege Perilous—and all the court knew that he would be the greatest knight the world had ever seen.

But even as he took his seat, Lancelot was struck by the beauty of Guinevere, which pierced his heart. As time passed, Lancelot and Guinevere fell deeply in love. Arthur either did not see it, or closed his eyes to it. But Merlin's prophecy was coming true: Guinevere would bring him much pain.

The knights of the Round Table became famous for their great adventures and prowess at fighting, and the most famous and skillful of all was Sir Lancelot. Yet for years, the Siege Perilous remained empty.

Sir Galahad

Then one day, a lady rode into court and demanded Lancelot ride into the forest with her. She led him to a convent where the nuns presented a young man.

"We have raised this boy," a nun said. "We wish you to make him a knight." Lancelot agreed, and the boy knelt to be knighted. Then Lancelot returned to court.

When the court gathered at the Round Table, they saw that new writing had appeared on the Siege Perilous:

"This seat will be filled 454 winters after the death of Jesus Christ."

"That's today!" Lancelot cried. They covered the seat with a rich cloth. At that moment, a squire rushed in.

"Come outside!" he cried out. "There is a miracle!"

Floating on the river that ran by the castle was a great red stone. Sticking out of the stone was Balin's sword.

The king urged Lancelot to take the sword, but the great knight refused.

"It's not for me," he said. "Anyone unworthy who tries to take it will suffer later." Even so, both Sir Gawain and Sir Perceval tried unsuccessfully to take it.

At dinner that night, all the doors and windows suddenly slammed shut as if blown by the wind. An old man appeared, leading the boy Lancelot had knighted. He wore an empty scabbard because he had no sword.

"I bring you a young knight, Galahad, who will accomplish great deeds for this court," the old man said.

Then he led the knight to the Siege Perilous and lifted the cloth that covered it. They saw new lettering: "This is the seat of Sir Galahad, the pure-hearted."

"This seat is yours," said the old man, and he left.

The king led Sir Galahad outside to see the sword that no knight could draw.

"They can't draw it because this is my adventure, and not theirs," said Sir Galahad, and easily drew the sword from the stone. Soon afterward, a lady rode up and said:

"This company will go on the greatest quest ever to take place in Britain, the quest to find the Holy Grail, the cup used by Jesus Christ for his last meal before he died. There will be many strange adventures to come. Sir Galahad will bring great honor to the court, but many knights will die." Then she rode away.

That night, the whole company had dinner together at the Round Table. Suddenly, there was a great rumbling of thunder, so loud that it seemed the castle would fall down. A beam of light seven times brighter than the sun shone straight into the room. The knights were silenced, looking at each other in wonder. Then the Holy Grail entered the room, carried by invisible hands and covered by a white cloth. The room filled with wonderful scents and every knight's plate was magically piled with his favorite food. In an instant, the Grail vanished and the knights could speak again.

The Quest for the Holy Grail

"Now," Sir Gawain said, "I swear that tomorrow I shall set off on the quest for the Holy Grail and shall not return until I have seen the Grail itself."

The other knights jumped up and made the same vow. King Arthur was grief-stricken.

"Alas!" he cried, "this wounds me deeply. I will never see you all gathered like this again. You are the best knights a king ever had, and yet you will be lost."

Early the next morning, amid much sadness, all the knights prepared to leave. They dressed in their armor, checked their lances and swords, and said their prayers. King Arthur wept to see his knights leave.

Soon, they went their separate ways. Sir Gawain rode a long time without coming across any adventures, and at last he met Sir Ector, who reported the same. The few challenges they had were evil, ending in the death of good men. Soon, Gawain and Ector met a holy hermit. They asked why they had such bad luck.

"You are too proud and wicked for this holy quest. You cannot succeed," said the hermit. "The Grail will test the virtuous, but you are not worthy."

And so it was for many of the knights. The hunt for the Holy Grail was the holiest quest ever attempted. Only the most virtuous knights could succeed and have adventures, but they also suffered hardships and trials.

Lancelot's Grail Adventures

After many days, Lancelot passed through a wild forest and came to a chapel. He peered through a broken door but couldn't get in, so he sat under a tree to sleep. Half asleep, he saw a sick knight on a bed, floating mysteriously to the chapel. Inside, as Lancelot watched throught the door, the Holy Grail appeared. The knight touched it and was healed. Even though he really wanted to approach the Grail, Lancelot's muscles would not move. He could not approach the Grail. The healed knight then took Lancelot's horse, shield, and sword and left.

When Lancelot fully woke, he heard a mysterious voice say, "Sir Lancelot, you are harder than stone, more bitter than wood, and more naked than a fig leaf. Go from these holy places!"

Lancelot was so distressed, he didn't know what to do. Weeping, he made his way to a place where a holy hermit lived. The hermit spoke to him:

"You were once the best knight in the world, but you have been proud and sinful. You are not fit to take part in such a holy quest." The hermit told him to wear a prickly shirt that scratched his skin and eat no meat while he was on the Grail quest. He also made him promise to give up all his earlier sins. Lancelot was more unhappy than he had been in his whole life.

Lancelot tried to rid himself of his pride, but it was not easy. One day, he saw an army of knights in white attacking a castle defended by knights in black. He rushed to help the black knights because they seemed the weakest, and that would bring him the most honor. He fought all day, until he was exhausted and could fight no more.

Lancelot was in despair because he had never been defeated before. A holy woman who lived in a chapel told him that he had shown his pride yet again, and he would have no success unless he could give it up.

A while later, Lancelot arrived at the sea and boarded a ship. It sailed away, taking him to a castle where he wandered around the empty rooms until he found one that he could not enter. He peered in, and saw the room suddenly fill with light. He would have gone in, but a mysterious voice told him to stay. So he watched from the doorway as the Holy Grail appeared. When he saw a priest struggling to carry the Grail, he rushed in to help but was struck down by a fiery wind.

For twenty-four days, he lay as if dead. When at last he awoke, he realized that with his vision of the Grail, his part in the quest was over, and so he returned to Camelot.

Now, very few knights remained in the quest for the Holy Grail.

Perceval's Grail Adventures

Finally, only Sir Perceval, Sir Bors, and Sir Galahad were left in the quest.

During the Grail quest, Sir Perceval was tempted by many demons that almost led to his destruction time after time. Once, a lady tried to lure him into love. But when Perceval made the sign of the cross, she vanished. He realized she had really been a demon.

Another time, Perceval traveled over a mountain by the sea. There was nothing there but wild beasts, and nowhere to rest. He went into a valley and there saw a snake dragging a young lion along by the neck. Soon, a larger lion came prowling and crying out, following the snake. When it caught up with the snake, the lion attacked it and they fought. Perceval thought the lion the nobler beast, so he took his sword and killed the snake.

The lion did not try to attack Perceval, but came and circled around him to show its gratitude. That night, the lion guarded Perceval as he slept. In the morning, the lion took its cub and left, and Perceval continued with his adventures.

At last, Perceval came to the sea and found a ship floating on it. It appeared to be waiting for him. He boarded the ship and it sailed away. He had no idea where it would take him, but knew that he must follow his own adventure.

Bors's Grail Adventures

During the course of his Holy Grail quest, Sir Bors had to make a terrible choice. As he rode through the forest, he saw his brother, Sir Lionel, being beaten by two knights. But before he could help him, he saw a man dragging a lady through the forest to attack her. He only had time to save one of them. As a knight, he could not leave the lady to suffer, so he chose to save her.

His brother survived. Bors was delighted when he met him again later—but Lionel would not forgive him and swore to kill him. As Bors tried to avoid fighting with him, Lionel killed first a hermit and then another knight who tried to intervene. At last Bors saw that he must fight him or die. But as they raised their swords, a cloud appeared between them and a voice commanded them to stop. They were both too afraid to move.

"Bors," the voice said, "flee! Leave this place and go to the sea where Sir Perceval awaits you."

So Bors left and went to the sea, where he found a boat and went aboard. Immediately, it set sail over the sea, and when night came, he slept. When he awoke, he searched the boat and found Sir Perceval, who was astonished to see him.

"So now we are only missing our friend Sir Galahad," Perceval said.

Galahad and the End of the Grail Quest

Galahad, as the purest of knights, had the most adventures on the holy quest. On one occasion, he came to a city besieged by enemies. He chose to help the losing side, but during the battle he unknowingly wounded Sir Gawain. Gawain remembered the sword he had tried to take from the floating red stone.

"Ah, it is just as I was told," said Gawain. "That sword would give a terrible wound to anyone who tried to take it and who was not the purest knight in the world. Now I know that my work on this quest is over." When he had recovered, he returned sadly to Camelot.

After the battle, Galahad was led by a lady to the ship in which Perceval and Bors waited for him. The ship carried them to Scotland, where they worked many miracles. One day, a vision directed them to a boat containing the Holy Grail, which was covered in red cloth. The boat carried them to the Holy Land. But there, the king of that land took them prisoner and kept them in a deep hole. For a year, until the wicked king died, the Grail fed them miraculously. The people then chose Galahad as the next king of the Holy Land. He ruled for one year and then asked God to take his soul, and so he died. Perceval stayed in the monastery where Galahad was buried, but Bors returned to Camelot and told the whole story to the court.

Lancelot and Guinevere

On his return to court, Lancelot took up his old ways again, forgetting his promise to live a virtuous life. One day, he argued with Guinevere, and she sent him away from the court. But soon she needed his help.

During May, it was Guinevere's custom to go out early in the morning to gather flowers. One morning, she took with her ten young knights, all dressed in green silk. Each knight was accompanied by a lady and a squire, plus two helpers. It was a large party that rode out to pick flowers.

A knight called Sir Meleagant lived nearby. He had loved Guinevere for a long time but was afraid of Sir Lancelot. When he saw her ride out with her group, but without Sir Lancelot, he decided it was his chance to kidnap her. He rode with a troop of eighty knights and attacked the group, and made them all come to his castle.

Guinevere, trapped in Meleagant's castle, persuaded a small child to smuggle out a message to King Arthur. She asked for Lancelot to be sent to rescue them, because Meleagant was so afraid of Lancelot.

But as Lancelot rode to the castle, Meleagant's treacherous knights attacked him and killed his horse, so that he had to continue on foot. It was hot, heavy work to walk in his armor with his sword and shield.

When a cart carrying wood came by, he made the driver take him to Meleagant's castle. He arrived shamefully in a cart, but nevertheless, Meleagant surrendered in fear. He then pleaded with Guinevere to ask Lancelot to spare his life, and she agreed to do so.

That night, Lancelot stayed in Meleagant's castle. The queen begged him to come to talk to her, but he cut his hand climbing through the barred window. Finding the blood, Meleagant denounced Guinevere, saying she had been unfaithful with an injured knight. Lancelot swore he would defend her in combat against that claim. But the cowardly Meleagant trapped Lancelot in a deep dungeon and kept him prisoner. Days passed, and Lancelot could not escape to save his queen. With no one to defend her, he knew that she would be put to death.

At last, the fire was lit for Guinevere to be burned, and the court was astonished that Lancelot did not arrive. Sir Lavaine agreed to defend Guinevere instead. Meanwhile, in prison, the lady who brought Lancelot food finally freed him—in exchange for a kiss. Lancelot galloped into the field just in time. The battle began, and Lancelot soon had Meleagant begging for his life and refusing to fight. So Lancelot tied his left arm behind his back, and they fought again. Even so, Lancelot quickly killed him, and the queen's name was cleared.

The End of it All

But Guinevere's name was soon in doubt again. Two knights, Aggravaine and Mordred, hated Lancelot. They believed Guinevere loved Lancelot more than the other knights and was betraying the king. Sir Gawain told them to stop the quarrel, but they wouldn't.

Aggravaine set a trap and caught Lancelot in Guinevere's room. Lancelot had to escape. He killed the first knight he met and took his armor. Then he fought his way out and escaped. Meanwhile, Aggravaine and Mordred demanded that the king have Guinevere burned for betraying him. News reached Lancelot of the plan, and he was furious. He gathered all his loyal knights and rode as fast as possible to the meadow near Camelot.

Guinevere was tied to a stake, and the fire was lit. Lancelot and his knights stormed from the forest and fell upon Arthur's knights. That day, many of the greatest knights of the Round Table lost their lives, including Aggravaine and Gawain's two brothers. Lancelot seized Guinevere and rode to his castle, Joyous Garde, to keep her safe until the king's anger cooled.

Mordred convinced Arthur to pursue Lancelot. When Gawain heard his brothers had died, he could no longer protect Lancelot.

"I will not rest until either I or he is dead," he said, wracked with sorrow and anger.

So Arthur gathered his knights, and Lancelot gathered those loyal to the queen and to him, and the fellowship of the Round Table was split asunder, knight against knight.

Arthur's army laid siege to Joyous Garde. Lancelot told the king that he would not fight him. But, urged on by Mordred and Gawain, Arthur insisted.

And so it began. Many brave and valiant knights fought against those who had once been their sworn friends. Spears shattered and swords clashed, blood ran over the field, and the cries of battle rang out all day. King Arthur repeatedly attacked Sir Lancelot, but Lancelot would not fight back. At last, Sir Bors knocked the king from his horse.

"Shall I put an end to this war?" he asked Lancelot, threatening to kill the king.

"No," Lancelot said, and helped the king back onto his horse. "My lord, stop this battle, I beg you."

Arthur rode away with tears in his eyes. "Alas, alas, that ever this war began," he wept. That night, both sides buried their dead.

Lancelot explained that it was not his wish to keep Guinevere from Arthur, but to save her from death. He took the queen back to Camelot and left her, saying:

"I will love and serve you to the end of my days, and if you have need of a knight, send for me."

So Lancelot left and everyone except Gawain wept.

Gawain persuaded the king to leave Mordred in charge of the country and attack Lancelot's lands. Every day, Gawain rode in battle against one or another of Lancelot's knights and eventually demanded that Lancelot meet him in battle. Lancelot had no choice.

Gawain had a special magical power. Each morning, his strength increased until noon and then returned to normal. Lancelot struggled against Gawain all morning, but when noon came, he soon gave him a terrible wound. But he refused to kill Gawain.

Gawain lay injured for weeks, but just as he was ready to battle Lancelot again, letters came from London that ended the siege. Mordred had falsely announced that Arthur and Lancelot were both dead, and that he was now king and would marry Guinevere. Guinevere had fled to the Tower of London.

Arthur rode to attack Mordred's huge army. The battle was long and bitter, and Gawain was mortally wounded. Dying, he spoke to King Arthur:

"It is my fault that you are still at war with Lancelot. If you were not, Mordred would be easily defeated. I am dying—bring me paper that I might write to Lancelot."

Gawain wrote to his old friend, saying he was sorry that he had been so proud and begging him to come and help Arthur defeat Mordred. Without his help, the kingdom was doomed.

And so Gawain died.

Arthur's army eventually pushed back Mordred's troops to Salisbury. They agreed that Arthur and Mordred should meet in the middle of the battlefield, each with fourteen knights. Arthur said that if any knight saw a sword drawn, the battle would start—he didn't trust Mordred. Mordred told his men the same. But during the meeting, a knight was bitten on the foot by a snake and, thinking nothing of it, drew his sword to kill it. The knights took it for treachery and drew their swords. And so the battle began. It was bitter and terrible—when night came, 100,000 men lay dead on the field. Arthur could see only Sir Bedevere and Sir Lucan left of his knights. And then he saw Mordred.

Their fight was short. Arthur quickly drove a spear through Mordred, wounding him fatally. But as he died, Mordred dealt Arthur a deadly blow to the head.

Arthur called Sir Bedevere and told him to take Excalibur and throw it into the lake.

"Come back and tell me what you see," he added.

Bedevere thought it a shame to throw such a fine sword away, so he hid it safely and went back to Arthur.

"What did you see?" Arthur asked.

"Just waves and ripples."

"Traitor!" Arthur said. "Go back and throw it in the lake like I told you."

Again, Bedevere hid the sword and Arthur was angry. So finally, Bedevere threw the sword with all his might.

A hand rose from the lake and caught it. Bedevere told this to King Arthur.

"Then take me there," Arthur said, and Bedevere carried him on his back to the lake. There, ladies dressed in black received him in a boat. Bedevere stood on the shore and cried out:

"Ah, my lord, what shall I do now? I trust only you."

"I am nothing to trust in," the king answered. "I have to go to Avalon now." And with that, the boat sailed into the darkness. Some people say that Arthur died, and others believe he will return to Britain.

Sir Lancelot found Guinevere living as a nun, and asked her to come away with him.

"That I cannot do," she said, "for this disaster was caused by us, and I must spend my last days repenting it. But you may go and marry a lady of your choosing."

"And that I cannot do," he answered, "for I will always be true to you. If this is how you will live, it is how I will live also."

Sir Lancelot, his heart broken, lived in a monastery until he learned of the death of Guinevere.

"My sorrow will have no end," he said, "for she was the noblest and most beautiful of women. And my pride has brought down the best two people in the world."

A few days later, Lancelot died. And so the fellowship of the Round Table ended, and the greatest knights that ever lived passed into history.

About the Author

Thomas Malory was born into a wealthy family between 1415 and 1418, in England. He inherited his father's land in 1433 or 1434. Malory served as a soldier, became a knight, and later a member of parliament. But he was not entirely respectable. He was imprisoned for many crimes, including robbery, kidnapping, and violence. During his time in prison, he wrote *Le Morte d'Arthur* (old French for "The Death of Arthur"), a series of stories based on King Arthur. He finished writing in 1469 and the book was published in 1485, after his death. He died in 1471.

Other titles in the *Illustrated Classics* series:
• *The Adventures of Tom Sawyer* • *Alice's Adventures in Wonderland* • *Anne of Green Gables* • *Black Beauty* • *Greek Myths* • *Gulliver's Travels* • *Heidi* • *A Little Princess* • *Little Women* • *Peter Pan* • *Pinocchio* • *Robin Hood* • *Robinson Crusoe* • *The Secret Garden* • *Sherlock Holmes* • *The Swiss Family Robinson* • *The Three Musketeers* • *Treasure Island* • *White Fang* • *The Wizard of Oz* • *20,000 Leagues Under The Sea*

Sandy Creek
NEW YORK

An Imprint of Sterling Publishing
387 Park Avenue South
New York, NY 10016

SANDY CREEK and the distinctive Sandy Creek logo
are registered trademarks of Barnes & Noble, Inc.

Text © 2015 by QEB Publishing, Inc.
Illustrations © 2015 by QEB Publishing, Inc.

This 2015 edition published by Sandy Creek.

ISBN 978-1-4351-5825-2

Editor: Carly Madden • Editorial Director: Victoria Garrard • Art Director: Laura Roberts-Jensen
Designer: Andrew Crowson

Manufactured in Guangdong, China
Lot #:
10 9 8 7 6 5 4 3 2 1
01/15